ANCIENT CIVILIZATIONS
EGYPT

By
Jane Pofahl

Illustrated By
Julie Anderson

Cover Illustration By
Mark Anthony

Publishers
T.S. Denison & Company, Inc.
Minneapolis, Minnesota 55431

T.S. Denison and Company, Inc.

Standard Book Number: 513-02191-4
Ancient Civilizations—Egypt
Copyright © 1993 by T.S. Denison & Co., Inc.
9601 Newton Avenue South
Minneapolis, Minnesota 55431

Introduction

History is the living record of the human race—exciting as it is varied. *The Time Traveler Series* will aid you as you teach the colorful history of ancient civilizations to your children and explore such topics as the development of language, early government, ancient cultures and art forms, scientific discoveries, and the historic personalities who helped shape our own present-day culture.

After each topic is presented, activity pages are provided for your children to implement suggested vocabulary, conduct further research, and provide creative answers/solutions to historical situations. Fun reproducible pages are also included to review the historical and cultural facts studied on the preceding pages.

Each book contains the following:

- topic information pages
- research/activity pages (including maps, charts, research topics, and creative thinking activities)
- reproducible activity pages
- time period stickers

The Time Traveler Series was created to spark the intrigue of your children and lay a foundation for enjoyable history instruction and learning. Have fun!

Table of Contents

A Historical Overview of Egypt

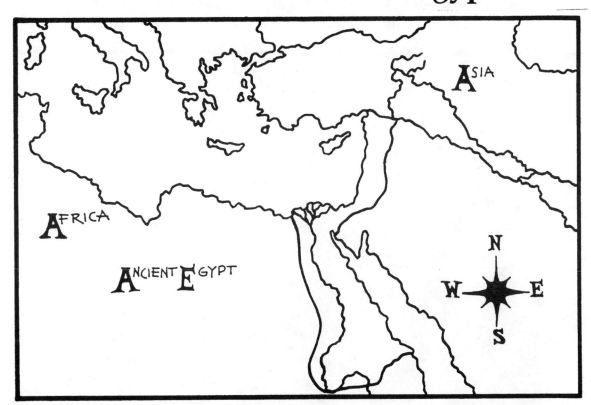

Ancient Egypt was the birthplace of one of the world's greatest civilizations. It was far more advanced than European tribes of the same time period, who were still in the Stone Age.

Located in the northeast corner of Africa, Egypt grew to be an important civilization for over three thousand years because of the Nile River. Running north and south through the center of the country, the Nile River would flood its banks each year and deposit silt on the farmlands to naturally refertilize the crops. The Nile River was also an important trade route which enabled the Egyptians to trade goods with their African and Mediterranean neighbors.

Egypt was originally divided into two kingdoms: Upper Egypt and Lower Egypt. The Pharaoh Menes united the kingdoms around 3100 B.C. After the union, the pharaoh was responsible for keeping Upper and Lower Egypt joined, thus avoiding a civil war between the Egyptians.

The pharaoh was more than a king. The Egyptians believed that he was the supreme ruler chosen by the gods to lead his people. The Egyptians also believed that when a man became the pharaoh, he also became a god. To keep the bloodline of the gods pure, pharaohs often married their sisters, mothers, and cousins.

The history of Egypt is divided into three major time periods: the *Old Kingdom* (when the pharaohs built the pyramids), the *Middle Kingdom* (when trading and military explorers were sent out to expand Egypt's boundaries), and the *New Kingdom* (ending with Queen Cleopatra losing her land to Augustus Caesar and Rome).

PHAROAH MENES

The Egyptians were a religious people. Their spiritual beliefs were a part of their daily life. They believed in life after death and developed a system of preserving dead bodies by mummification.

The Egyptians were also a hard-working people. Egypt was the first agricultural nation of the world. They invented a written and spoken language, the world's first national government, a basic math system, a 365-day calendar, a large-scale irrigation system, and papyrus writing paper. The most impressive achievements of the Egyptians are the huge pyramids, located along the Nile River banks.

Geography

Ancient Egypt was a long, narrow country located in the northeast corner of Africa. The Nile River flowed north through the center of the country. The river split into many fan-shaped channels at the mouth, or end, of the river, forming the Nile Delta. Every year the Nile River overflowed its banks and flooded the valley, leaving a rich layer of silt to refertilize the topsoil. The Egyptians also used the Nile River as a means of transportation and trade, as well as irrigation for their crops. Egypt has earned the name "the gift of the Nile" because of the many ways the Nile River has benefited this country.

Egypt was divided into two regions, known as Upper and Lower Egypt. The northern area, including the Nile Delta, was called Lower Egypt because the elevation of the land at the delta was low, at sea level. All the land south of the pyramids had a higher elevation and was considered Upper Egypt.

Egypt possessed many natural protective barriers. The Mediterranean Sea lay to the north and the Red Sea lay to the east. Ancient Egyptians depended on deserts in the east, south, and west, as well as mountains on the eastern coast to protect them from invaders.

Geography

RESEARCH QUESTIONS

1. In a dictionary, find the following words: *channel, delta, silt, topsoil, transportation, irrigation, benefit, elevation, pyramid, protective, barrier,* and *invader.* Define each word and use it in a sentence.

2. The Nile River began flooding its banks in June during the rainy season and usually went down in September. From October to February, Egyptians planted crops. Harvest time was from March to May. Make a chart showing the rainy and growing seasons for ancient Egypt by the month.

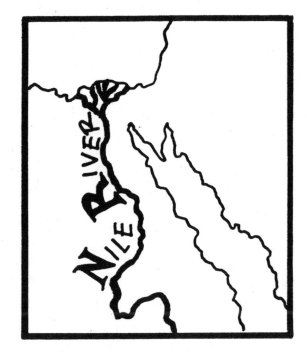

PROJECTS

1. You are a merchant in ancient times. You sell your goods along the Nile River. Do you think you will sell more goods in Upper Egypt or in Lower Egypt? Why?

2. You are an invader and you want to attack ancient Egypt. How will you do it? Show on a map how you will invade a country surrounded by seas, deserts, and mountains.

3. List all the ways the Nile River helped the ancient Egyptians. Then write a paragraph using the following sentence starter: "Egypt was known as the 'Gift of the Nile' because _____."

Egypt

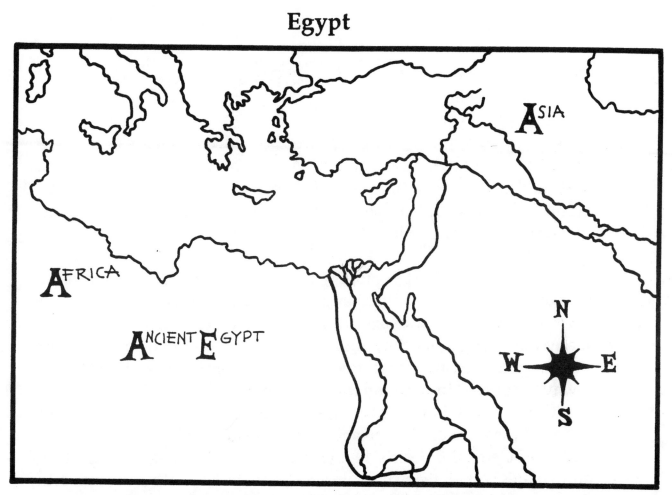

1. Identify the following on your map (refer to a map of ancient Egypt in an encyclopedia):

    - Nile River
    - Nile Delta
    - Nubian Desert
    - Red Sea
    - Lower Egypt

    - City of Memphis
    - Libyan Desert
    - Mediterranean Sea
    - Upper Egypt
    - Red Sea Highlands

    - City of Thebes
    - City of Luxor
    - Arabian Desert
    - Great Pyramid at Giza

2. Draw a box in the lower left corner of your map and title it "Map Key." Include in your key the symbols you use to identify deserts and mountain ranges.

3. Shade the water blue, the deserts tan, and the mountain ranges gray. Outline the ancient Egyptian Empire in red.

4. Why would it be important for a pharaoh to unite Upper Egypt and Lower Egypt? _____
    _____

5. Why was Upper Egypt to the south and Lower Egypt to the north? _____
    _____

Gods and Goddesses

Before Upper and Lower Egypt were joined, each area was made up of separate tribes who worshipped gods of nature: the sun, the wind, and the earth, for example. All of these gods were thought to have animal forms and animal-like qualities as well, such as the strength of a bull or the bravery of a lion.

As time passed, the Egyptians gave some of the gods and goddesses human forms, or part animal and part human forms. The king of the gods was Amon, who was also the god of the powerful city, Thebes. After many years, the legends of Amon were combined with the myths of Re, the sun-god, to create a single god: Amon-Re. Osiris, the god of the dead, always appeared in mummy form. When he was killed by his brother, Set, Osiris was reborn with help from his wife, Isis, and Egyptians believed they too could live again after death if they preserved their bodies as Osiris did. Osiris' helper was Anubis, who had a dog's head and a man's body. Sobek, the water-god, had the head of a crocodile. Nūt, the sky-goddess, looked similar to a huge cow; and Re, the sun-god, rode on Nūt's back across the sky during the day. The Egyptians believed that the gods and goddesses were happy, sad, angry, and jealous—just like humans!

Gods and Goddesses

RESEARCH QUESTIONS

1. In a dictionary, find the following words: *worship, qualities, bravery, legend, myth, appear, mummy, preserve,* and *jealous.* Define each word and use it in a sentence.

2. Find out more about the Egyptian gods and goddesses. List the duties performed by the following: *Amon-Re, Osiris, Isis, Thoth, Sobek, Anubis, Ptah, Hathor, Nūt,* and *Shu.*

3. How did the Egyptians come to worship deities that were half human and half animal? Research the development of Egyptian gods and goddesses. Report your findings to the class.

PROJECTS

1. Amon was the patron god of Thebes. You think that your Egyptian city needs a god or goddess to protect it as well. Choose an Egyptian god or goddess, and create a myth that connects the deity with your city.

2. Design your own Egyptian god or goddess. Draw him or her, and write a description of his or her duties.

3. Using the god or goddess you just invented, write a poem about her or him.

ANUBIS

King Tut

Did you know that Tutankhamen, or King Tut for short, was called "The Boy King"? He became a pharaoh when he was only nine years old, in the year 1361 B.C.

King Tut lived in a beautiful palace in the city of Thebes. He had servants who did everything he commanded because he was the pharaoh, and the Egyptians believed he was a god, not a human being.

A typical day for King Tut began in the audience chamber of the palace, where he sat on a throne of gold, silver, and jewels, and wore a heavy gold headpiece shaped like a flame. Ambassadors from foreign countries bowed before him and brought him riches. Egyptians came to him to settle their disputes, since he was their wise god-pharaoh. In the afternoon, he went to the temple to lead his people in a three-hour worship ceremony. After the formal dinner in the evening, the king might have had time to see his wife, Ankheshamen, who was two years younger than he.

King Tut died when he was only nineteen years old. No one knows for sure if he died by accident, illness, or his enemies. His burial chamber was found by Britain's Howard Carter in 1922. The treasures of King Tut's tomb can be seen today in Cairo, Egypt.

King Tut

RESEARCH QUESTIONS

1. In a dictionary, find the following words: *pharaoh, command, typical, audience, chamber, throne, ambassador, foreign, dispute, temple, ceremony, formal,* and *burial*. Define each word and use it in a sentence.

2. Find out about how *Howard Carter* and his expedition discovered King Tut's tomb. Report your findings in writing or by pretending to be Howard Carter and telling your story to the group.

3. King Tut is famous because his tomb was found intact, or untouched, by grave robbers. Find out more about the treasures in King Tut's tomb. Using resource books, make a picture catalog of items in his tomb.

PROJECTS

1. Make a mask like King Tut's golden mask. Blow up a balloon, then dip strips of newspaper in a flour paste and mold the strips over the balloon to create the shape of the mask. Allow the balloon to dry, then paint a mask face.

2. Would you have liked to trade places with young King Tut? Why or why not?

3. You are a pharaoh in Egypt and you don't want robbers in your tomb. Write a description of how you would hide your tomb from grave robbers.

King Tut's Tell-Tale Diary

You are the sacred ruler of Egypt and the Nile River region, Pharaoh Tutankhamen. You prefer to be called Tut. All day long you have to do what your advisors tell you to do—receive ambassadors from foreign countries, listen to the complaints of your subjects, and preside over long worship ceremonies. It is now evening and you are finally left alone to write in your diary. What are you thinking and feeling?

MY DIARY BY TUT

_____

_____

_____

_____

_____

_____

_____

_____

_____

_____

_____

_____

Life After Death

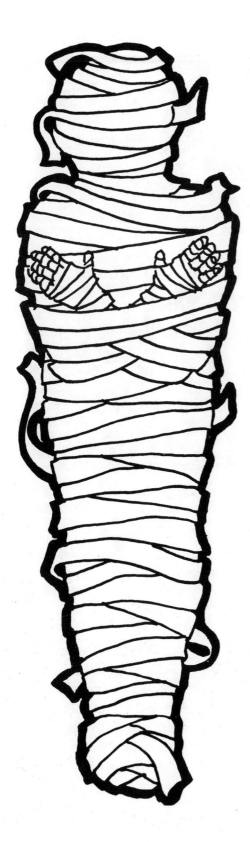

The ancient Egyptians believed in an afterlife of beauty, peace, and contentment. Since most Egyptians' lives were filled with back-breaking work and few comforts, they looked forward to their deaths as a release from this lifetime. They also believed their souls would need to use their bodies again, so the Egyptians invented a process to embalm their bodies called mummification.

Wealthy people could afford better mummifying than the poor. The process lasted up to seventy days. After the body was washed and covered with scented oils, the liver and kidneys were removed and placed in separate canopic jars, which would be put in the mummy's coffin later. The brains were removed carefully, but the heart was left in the body because the Egyptians believed it was the mind and would be needed immediately in the next life. Then the body was wrapped in either linen or rough cotton strips and a sticky, tar-like mixture was poured over the cloth strips to form a protective outer covering for the body. When the mixture hardened, the mummy was placed in a wooden coffin, which was carved and painted to resemble the person. The mummy was then laid in its tomb, along with many objects the Egyptians thought it would need for daily use in the next lifetime, such as tools, jewelry, furniture, religious statues, and food.

Life After Death

RESEARCH QUESTIONS

1. In a dictionary, find the following words: *contentment, soul, process, embalm, mummification, wealthy, afford, scented, canopic, coffin, protective, carve, resemble, tomb,* and *statue.* Define each word and use it in a sentence.

2. Find out more about the mummification process. How did they wrap the bodies?

3. The Egyptian symbol for eternal life was an *ankh.* Draw an ankh and find out how it was used.

PROJECTS

1. You are the artist in charge of designing the dead pharaoh's tomb walls. Draw the scenes you plan to paint depicting the pharaoh's deeds in his lifetime.

2. Egyptians believed that the pharaohs lived after they died and that the pharaohs would need certain items in their tombs. You must decide what objects will be placed in the pharaoh's tomb. List all objects necessary for the pharaoh's duties and comfort (don't forget food!).

The A-Maze-ing Mummy Tomb

Hassan has a problem. He is about to enter the tomb of the Most Majestic Supreme Pharaoh Phooten-Phooen, or Phoo-Phoo for short. The pharaoh left very specific instructions before he died. One of them was to have food brought to him daily by his servants. Today is Hassan's turn. However, no one told him how to find Phoo-Phoo's secret burial chamber once he was inside the tomb. As he walked up to the tomb, he saw these symbols next to the entrance:

He figures that they are clues to lead to Phoo-Phoo's tomb. Follow the clues in order with Hassan to find the burial chamber of Pharaoh Phoo-Phoo.

Daily Life of Workers

Life in ancient Egypt was difficult for the poor. They worked long hours for goods that they could exchange in the marketplace for the products they needed. Even though many of them were skilled craftsmen, they were looked down upon by the wealthy.

Because the Nile River could irrigate crops, agriculture was a major trade and many workers were farmers. Egypt was famous for its finely-woven linen cloth—both men and women were expert weavers. Large numbers of workers served the pharaoh, priests, and the wealthy. Still others were involved in service at the necropolis, the place of the burial tombs for the kings and the wealthy.

Children had little time for play. Boys learned a trade from their fathers, and girls were taught to care for the home and family by their mothers.

Women and girls wore straight, sheath-like dresses of rough, unbleached linen. Men and boys wore short cloth kilts.

The Egyptian workers' sun-dried brick homes were usually one story high, one room wide, and included a basement and four rooms. They had little furniture. Stairs led to the flat rooftop so that the family could enjoy the cool night air after the sun went down.

Daily Life of Workers

RESEARCH QUESTIONS

1. In a dictionary, find the following words: *exchange, skilled, agriculture, expert, priest, necropolis, trade, sheath,* and *kilt.* Define each word and use it in a sentence.

2. You can find out more about Egyptian workers' lives by looking at pictures of the walls in tombs. Write a paragraph about what you have learned.

3. Find out more about the kinds of work performed at the Necropolis. Write a report about your findings.

PROJECTS

1. Imagine you are living in ancient Egypt. What does your family do for a living? Draw a picture showing a typical day for your family in Egyptian art style.

2. Describe a game you made up to play on the flat rooftop when you relaxed there at night with your family.

3. You live in ancient Thebes. You know that when you grow up you will be a servant to the pharaoh, the priests, or a wealthy family. For whom would you choose to serve? Why?

Daily Life of Workers Crossword

ACROSS:

2. River that runs through Egypt.
6. Worker trained in a specific craft.
10. The business of farming.
11. Short, wraparound cloth worn by men in Egypt.
13. Trade one good or service for another.

DOWN:

1. Men and women who wove beautiful cloths for a living.
3. Place where the family joined in the evening to cool off.
4. To water, usually crops.
5. Straight dresses worn by women in Egypt.
7. Burial tomb site of the kings.
8. Ruler of Egypt.
9. Very little of this was found in the homes of workers.
12. Common material used for clothing in Egypt.

Daily Life of the Wealthy

The wealthy enjoyed a life of comfort and reward in ancient Egypt. Men were busy all day as merchants, trading along the Nile River with Nubians, Libyans, and Syrians. Others supervised the daily workings of gigantic farms. Many of the wealthiest and most powerful men in Egypt were priests. Boys from well-to-do families were taught to read and write, which helped guarantee them a successful future. Women of the upper class had many privileges. They could own land, run businesses, testify in a court of law, and bring charges against men. Women oversaw the running of the households and gave the servants instructions for daily menus and child care.

Children were allowed much playtime. Girls practiced singing and dancing. When they were not studying, boys wrestled and played army.

Women and girls wore straight dresses of beautiful linen and a lot of jewelry. At parties, women wore cones of incense on their heads that melted slowly and gave off a pleasing scent. Men and boys wore linen kilts. Both men and women wore eye make-up made from black ashes.

The brick and wood homes of the wealthy contained many rooms, as well as a walled garden and a shrine for a favorite god.

WEALTHY EGYPTIAN HOME & GARDEN

Daily Life of the Wealthy

RESEARCH QUESTIONS

1. In a dictionary, find the following words: *merchant, supervise, gigantic, guarantee, success, future, privilege, testify, wrestle, greasy, incense, ashes,* and *shrine.* Define each word and use it in a sentence.

2. Find out about typical Egyptian foods. Make up a menu for a fancy Egyptian feast.

3. Find out more about the goods traded by wealthy Egyptians. Make a chart showing a variety of Egyptian goods that were traded with their Mediterranean neighbors.

THE EGYPTIAN
FINE DINING

APPETIZERS
FRUITS .... FRESH
VEGETABLES...... FRESH

ENTREES
WHEAT - CURRENT CROP PRICE

FARM ANIMAL OF THE DAY
[COW]

VEGETABLES.... FRESH
FRUIT......... FRESH

BEVERAGES
WATER
WINE

WE OFFER A FINE DESSERT ASSORTMENT

PROJECTS

1. Make a model of a wealthy Egyptian's home. Label the rooms and list their contents.

2. Design a costume of an Egyptian woman's party outfit.

3. You are a child of a wealthy family in Egypt. Write in your journal about a typical day in your childhood.

4. You are an artist in ancient Egypt. You are hired to make a gold and jeweled neckpiece for a wealthy merchant. Draw and color your design for the neckpiece.

Lifestyles of the Rich and Egyptian

The wealthiest man in your district, Akhenose, has asked you to design the floor plan for his new luxury home in the valley. He wants:

- The square home built around an inner courtyard, resembling a doughnut (with the courtyard as the doughnut center).
- The large rooms to have windows and doors opening into the courtyard.
- The structure is to be only one story high.

Pretend that you are looking down at the house (a bird's eye view) and use the space below to draw your floorplan design.

Written Language

To read and write, we have to learn twenty-six letters and put them together to make words. An ancient Egyptian child had to learn *hundreds* of separate picture symbols, or hieroglyphics, and put them in the right order to make a sentence—not an easy task!

Young boys spent years learning the complicated system of hieroglyphics, which were pictures and symbols that could stand for either a word or a whole idea. For example, the word for "house" would look like the outline of a house. Hieroglyphics could be read from right to left, left to right, or top to bottom in columns.

Egyptians wrote on thin scrolls of papyrus. These scrolls were made by cutting thin strips off the center of papyrus reeds, which grew along the Nile River bank. The strips were laid across each other and were beaten with a mallet until the natural juices, acting like glue, bound them together. When the papyrus paper sheets dried, they were pasted together into a long roll. To write on papyrus, a scribe would dip a reed pen in water and rub it over a piece of charcoal to make ink. For important documents, the Egyptians also wrote on moistened clay tablets with a reed pen.

Written Language

RESEARCH QUESTIONS

1. In a dictionary, find the following words: *symbol, hieroglyphics, complicated, scroll, papyrus, reed, mallet, bound, scribe, charcoal, document, moisten,* and *tablet.* Define each word and use it in a sentence.

2. We can understand hieroglyphics today because of the *Rosetta Stone,* discovered in Egypt by Napoleon's army in 1798. Find out about this stone. How does it help us translate hieroglyphics into English?

3. Research the development of written language. Make a timeline showing the language accomplishments of ancient civilizations.

PROJECTS

1. Make a poster of simple hieroglyphic symbols and label them.

2. You are the first person to discover how to pound papyrus reeds into paper. What will you do with your discovery?

3. Learn how paper is made. Contact your local library for information. (Paper-making kits are available in most hobby stores.)

Create Your Own Hieroglyphics

Many civilizations have used picture-writing throughout history. Cavemen in France, Mesopotamians in the Middle East, Egyptians along the Nile River, and the American Indians in the Southwest have all used picture-writing to express their thoughts and record events.

Hieroglyphics was a sophisticated system of pictures and symbols used in ancient Egypt to communicate information. You can draw your own symbols to stand for words and ideas to create a hieroglyphic language.

In the boxes below, draw symbols and write their meanings on the line. Don't forget to include symbols for people, weather, food, animals, and objects in your world. One is done for you to help you get going.

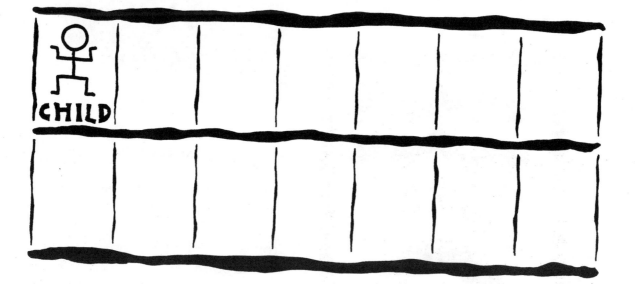

"Write" a sentence using as many symbols as possible.

Painting and Sculpture

We know a lot about Egyptian art today because of the beautiful detailed paintings and finely crafted sculpture left in the tombs of the pharaohs. Egyptian artists were also hired to decorate the walls of the temples for the gods.

When drawing people, Egyptians used two-point perspective; that is, they only showed the height and width of people. Since people actually have height, width, and depth, Egyptian art figures look more like flat cartoon characters than real people.

Scenes showing daily life, festivals, military battles, and important occasions were not only for decoration. Egyptians believed these scenes would come to life in the next world, so they always pictured themselves as attractive, rich, brave, and successful!

Egyptians reached a highly advanced level of sculpture as well. Beautiful figures sculpted from wood, ivory, bronze, gold, and turquoise have been found in tombs. One of the most famous sculptures in the world is the head of Queen Nefertiti. Another famous artwork is the Great Sphinx, a huge statue of a man's head on a lion's body, which guards the pyramids near Giza.

Painting and Sculpture

RESEARCH QUESTIONS

1. In a dictionary, find the following words: *detail, crafted, sculpture, hire, perspective, festival, military, decoration, scene, attractive,* and *advanced.* Define each word and use it in a sentence.

2. Look at pictures of the walls from Egyptian tombs. In the Egyptian style of drawing, sketch a scene from your life for your tomb.

3. Find out more about *two-point perspective.* Present your findings to the class and include drawings of two-point perspective to illustrate your speech.

PROJECTS

1. Make your own model of Nefertiti's head using modeling clay.

2. Use a plastic knife to carve an Egyptian object from a bar of soap, such as a mummy or a fishing boat.

3. A *cartouche* is a tablet with a border, used as a nameplate. Using Egyptian symbols, make a cartouche for your own name.

4. You are a sculptor in ancient Egypt. The pharaoh orders you to design a statue that will guard the entrance to his tomb, similar to the Sphinx, but of your own design. Draw the design for the statue.

Achievements

The greatest achievement of the Egyptians was the pyramids. There are about eighty pyramids along the banks of the Nile River and the largest of them all is the Great Pyramid, built by King Khufu in about 2500 B.C. It originally stood 482 feet high. The pyramids functioned as huge burial tombs for the Egyptians' dead pharaohs and queens.

The Egyptians were also excellent ship-builders. They used the Nile River like a highway to transport people and goods to foreign lands. The first ships were made out of bundles of papyrus reeds tied together to make canoe-like vessels. As the shipping trade flourished, the hulls of the ships were made of cedar, and oars and sails were added for greater speed.

Although the system of hieroglyphics is much different than that of our own language, these pictures and symbols served as one of the first written languages in the world.

By watching the night sky, ancient Egyptians developed a calendar based on the flooding of the Nile River.

Achievements

RESEARCH QUESTIONS

1. In a dictionary, look up the following words: *achievement, function, transport, bundle, vessel, flourish, hull,* and *system.* Define each word and use it in a sentence.

2. Draw a picture of what the inside of a pyramid looks like.

3. The ancient Egyptians made detailed drawings of the positions of the stars in the night sky. Create your own chart of star formations using encyclopedias and astronomy books.

PROJECTS

1. Make a pyramid out of sugar cubes, glue or paste, toothpicks, and poster board.

2. Create a model or a drawing of an Egyptian trading ship; include a sail and oars.

3. If you could decide on what day each new year would start, what would it be? Why?

See Egypt First!

It is the seventh year in the reign of the Most Magnificent Pharaoh Ramalama, and His Most Magnificence is not pleased. He feels that Egypt is not making as much gold and silver from tourists and travelers as it used to. You gently point out to him that the Sphinx is old news, but he will hear none of it. He orders you to come up with an informational brochure, including full-color pictures, advertising the achievements and tourist attractions of Egypt. Not wanting to upset His Glorious Splendidness any further you:

1. Draw as many tourist attractions from Egypt as you can think of on a piece of scratch paper. Include pictures such as pyramids, the Sphinx, the Nile River, and camels.

2. Think up a catchy slogan to attract tourists to Egypt. Last year's slogan was, "Pyramids, Mummies, and a Whole Lot More!" Write your new slogan on the scratch paper as well.

3. Take a piece of 8 1/2" by 11" white paper, turn it so that it is long from side to side, and fold it into thirds.

4. Turn the paper so that it is long from top to bottom. Decide which section will be the cover of your brochure. Write your catchy slogan on the front cover and draw a picture to illustrate your slogan.

5. Open up your brochure and continue to draw and color pictures of tourist attractions and achievements from Egypt. Use the ideas you sketched out on your scratch paper.

6. After drawing and coloring each picture, write at least one sentence under it to describe what it is or why it is significant to Egypt.

Time Line of Ancient Egyptian History

2686–2181 B.C.   ***Old Kingdom***
Menes united Upper and Lower Egypt; the pyramids, Sphinx, and the tombs of the kings were built.

2181–2040 B.C.   *First Intermediate Period*
Weak pharaohs in the later Old Kingdom period led to over two hundred years of chaos; princes of Thebes restored control.

2040–1786 B.C.   ***Middle Kingdom***
Trading and military expeditions sent out to extend Egypt's southern borders.

1786–1567 B.C.   *Second Intermediate Period*
Weak kings destroyed the prosperity of the Middle Kingdom; Egypt was invaded by the Hyksos, who ruled for two hundred years.

1570–1085 B.C.   ***New Kingdom***
Again, rulers from Thebes drove out the invaders; a four-hundred-year span of prosperity and achievement ensued; King Tut (r. 1361–1352 B.C.)

1085–332 B.C.   *Late Dynastic Period*

323-30 B.C.   *Ptolemaic Dynasty*
Cleopatra was the last Egyptian ruler; after her death, Egypt became a province of Rome.